CHESTER
ELECTRIC LIGHTING STATION

From steam and hydro: the illuminating story of Chester
streetlighting and Britain's first rural electricity supply

TEXT, RESEARCH AND PUBLICATION BY

©2002

GORDON EMERY
27 Gladstone Road, Chester CH1 4BZ
01244 377955

PRINTED BY

MFP DESIGN & PRINT
Stretford, Manchester, M32 0JT

CREDITS

Without the combined efforts of many people, their signatures on a petition, the coverage by the press, particularly the Chester Standard, and the (eventual) backing of Chester City Council planning officers, this book would never have been researched or written.

Most of all, the building remains because of the efforts of the Canal Basin Community Forum action committee, (of which I am proud to be a member) and in particular Avril Coady and Julie Shaw-Mackintosh, who never gave up even after demolition permission had been granted. Others who wrote to protect the building include John Ebo, Len Morgan, Michael Hoddinot, Jim Mackintosh and Tony Bowerman. Our local councillor, Steve Davies, managed to get the final plans, including the retention of the building, through council.

Thanks for photographs in this book go to Chester Community History and Heritage, (inside the electric light building) and the Science & Society Picture Library at the Science Museum, London (electrical household machinery). The photographs from the former Electric Showroom designs, (identified by the science staff at Queen's Park High School) and the insulator, are by Mike Penney.

Special thanks to George Wimpey Northwest Ltd. creators of the 'Minerva' development which incorporates the refurbishment of the Electric Lighting Station, for their help in the production of this book.

Lamp
Image from the front of the former
Electric Showroom in Foregate Street.

Insulator found in the Electric Lighting Station.

Courtesy of Terry Hughes

CONTENTS

Static electricity

Excerpts from council minutes, letters and newspapers of the time make up this book. Long extracts are paraphrased. The author's comments are in {}. In 1882, after getting the initial Bill on electric power passed through Parliament, along with other corporations, Chester Corporation dithered and bumbled, while stopping private companies breaking into their monopoly, before finally supplying the goods in 1896. In the meantime, councillors took expense-paid trips by rail to Brighton and other English cities to view electric power stations.

The city looked at a variety of sites for their station - one resulted in the Cathedral purchasing it to keep as an open space (nowadays it is a car park) and prevent its use for industry - they also looked at various kinds of electrical supply and even employed a noteworthy electrical engineer who resigned when they lost confidence in him, before finally accepting the fairly obvious, but detailed, comments of the famous Lord Kelvin.

One letter puts plainly the views of Chester merchants, up in arms to get the project moving, their city years behind the times before electricity was finally provided.

Under these circumstances it is, perhaps, surprising that Chester went on to lead Britain in supplying electricity to rural areas. This was probably due, in part, to the vision and dedication of the two electrical engineers for the city, Thurston and Britton. These men made remarkable advances despite low pay and little reward for their efforts in coping with rapidly increasing demand.

So here is the story of Chester electric lighting and power. Trams have been included, but not in detail, nor the connection to the Central Electricity Board (the National Grid) in 1926 and the ultimate changeover to AC (Alternating Current) in the 1930s. For those who want to read more, minutes from 1900 are available in print at the Community History and Heritage Centre in the former St Michael's Church, Bridge Street, while the original handwritten minutes are at Cheshire and Chester Archives, Duke Street, together with the papers of Sydney Britton, including the article from the Washington Daily News.

The original Electric Lighting Station had a five bay frontage, a porch added in 1900, then an extension with wings at both ends was added as demand for electric power increased. A small extension was made on the original front when more office space was needed.

Chester Hydro-electric Power Station is now a water pumping station adjacent to Old Dee Bridge. (See 'Miller of Dee' by Roy Wilding for the history of that site.)

From candles to gaslight

Council minutes 1503

'ebry man that hath byne mayre or shriffes of the citie of Chester and allso all innkeepers as well they that habe sygnez as they that habe no sygnez shall habe hanging at ther dore a lantorne wyth a candyll bryning in it every nyghte from that it be furst nyght unto the oure of 8 of the clocke, that is to wyt from the feste of All Sayntes unto the fest of the Puryfaccion of Our Lady then nexte ffolying yerlye' (Nov 1-Feb 2)

Council minutes 1537

'Ordered, That all Public Houses shall hang out their lantornes and candles from six of the clocke in the evening until nine of the clocke every night betwen the feast of All Saints and the Purification of the Virgin Mary'

1617

Adam Caine the Beadle was paid 2s6d for 'providing of candles to the city's lantern at the new stairs'.

1704

Two convex lamps to be provided and set up at the city's charge - one at the corner of the new Pentice and the other at the Exchange. Regulations that councillors and publicans should hang lanterns were cancelled on a 25-24 vote.

1724

'payd for mending the Lanthorn in the Pentice 0:1:6'

1737

Nathaniel Hall leased a messuage with appurtenances on the north side of Eastgate Street and was required to: *'set up before the front of the said messuage a Lamp with convex Glasses of the same sort and size as is now in the City of London and supply the same with oil and keep the same burning from three large weeks [wicks] of Cotton...to the hour of ten between the tenth day of September and the tenth day of March'.*

1762 Act

'And it is hereby further enacted by the Authority aforesaid, That if any Person or Persons shall wantonly, wilfully, carelesly, or maliciously, break, throw down, extinguish, damage, displace or spoil any lamp that shall be hung out, fired or set up to light the Streets, Rows or Passages, in the said City ... forfeit the sum of five pounds'.

(1801 London had its first gas street lighting.)

1853 Assembly minutes

'that the recomendation of the Watch Committee to accept Mr Highfield's offer to light the City for two years with not less than two hundred and eighty three and not more than Two hundred and ninety-three Batwing Burners at a cost not exceeding £786 per annum being the expense of lighting the City last year be accepted.'

1854

An order was made to change some of the Batwings to fishtails.

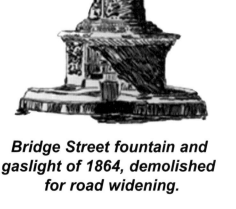

Bridge Street fountain and gaslight of 1864, demolished for road widening.

Harnessing the power of electricity

*Image from the front of the former
Electric Showroom in Foregate Street.*

Holding on to power

Upon the recommendation of the Watch Committee: Ordered: That the council do join the other corporations appearing by Counsel before the Select Committee upon "The Electric Lighting Bill" and defray apportionably (sic) with such other Corporations according to the assessable value of the Property in the Boroughs represented any costs incurred.
Resolved: That as regards the amendment sought to be obtained in the Bill to provide "that no application for a License or Provisional Order on the part of any Company or person shall be made in respect of all or any part of the district of a Local Authority without Three months notice in writing to such Local Authority" it is the opinion of this Council that Six Months notice should be required instead of Three; and therefore that a strong endeavour should be made to enlarge the term of the Notice from Three Months to Six Months'.

Quarterly meeting of the Council 9th August 1882
Town Clerk's Office, Dale Street.   Liverpool, 4th August 1882.

Dear Sir   Electric Lighting
  Referring to my Letter to you of the 2nd August I now hear from my Agents that this bill has been read a second time in the House of Lords and that an attempt is being made to get it referred to a Select Committee. I send a draft of Petition which the corporation of Liverpool will present and I shall be glad if your Corporation shall do the same.
  Will you kindly have the Petition engrossed on parchment and sealed and forward it to Messrs Sherwood & Co of 7 St George St. Westminster.S.W. as soon as possible.
                    Yours truly
                       For the Town Clerk
                          G.J.Atkinson
   The Town Clerk of Chester

The letter overleaf was read and a petition regarding "An Act to facilitate and regulate the supply of Electricity for lighting and other purposes in Great Britain and Ireland" authorised for presentation, asking that no corrections or omissions be made in the House of Lords.

Monthly Meeting of the Council 10th January 1883

Watch Committee authorised to object to a Provisional Order by the Union Electric Light and Power Company Limited to erect and maintain Electric lines and works.

Quarterly Meeting of the Council 14th February 1883

The Board of Trade had intimated that they would not grant an order to a private company without the Corporation's acceptance.

Quarterly meeting of the Council 14th August 1889

The following recommendation of the Watch Committee having been considered vis: Recommendation that application be made by the council to the Board of Trade for a Provisional Order under the Electric Lighting Acts 1882 and 1888...
Ordered that a special Meeting to be convened accordingly.

Special Meeting of the Council of the City of Chester (being the Local Authority for the purposes of the Electric Lighting Acts 1882 and 1888 of the Urban Sanitary District of the City of Chester) 18th September 1889
Resolved that application be made to the Board of Trade for a Provisional Order.

Pylon
Image from the front of the former
Electric Showroom in Foregate Street.

Electric bill causes a shock

<u>Watch Committee 8th January 1891</u>

The Chester Electric Lighting Provision Order 1890 had gone through Parliament on 5th January 1891. The London printer's bill (Nicholls) was for the {enormous} sum of £229-6-0 with £94-10-00 for proofing and corrections. {This when average bills for services through council committees were around £5.} It had been referred back to the Watch Committee for further particulars.

<u>Watch Committee 5th February 1891</u>

The Town Clerk reported the result of enquiries made of the following towns which had obtained Provisional Orders on the same session of Parliament: Blackburn, Derby, Manchester, Nottingham and Worcester.

Also Nicholls' account had been checked and the council had received a letter stating that their charges were normal from Wm Clowes & Son Ltd., and a letter from Martin & Leslie to say that Nicholls were the most respectable Parliamentary printers and it was difficult to compare this work with other bills.

No comment could be obtained from the House (of Parliament). It was recommended that the bill be paid.

Insulated wire
Image from the front of the former
Electric Showroom in Foregate Street.

Current works

Special Meeting of the Watch Committee 13th August 1891

The committee was specially convened to discuss establishing Electric Lighting. An inspection of the Bradford works and other places was planned.

(In November that year it was ordered that the night duty police constables be provided with hot coffee during the winter months.)

Special Meeting of the Watch Committee 24th December 1891

An Inspection of Electric Lighting in Brighton, St Pancras, Eastbourne and Brompton took place between November 24th and 29th. {Free holidays for some!}

Brighton & Hove Company Central Station had been providing a high pressure alternating current for 10 years but the streets were still lit by gas, and tradesmen were not supplied with electric light. Brighton Corporation also supplied a low pressure continuous current. Larger hotels provided their own. 5,000 lamps were now used at one time. Welsh steam coal was the preferred fuel at 22s per ton. A continuous current system was used. Brighton Council advise keeping the Order in the hands of the council as they have great faith in the future of Electric light. The cost of lamps is double that of gas but it is brighter, cleaner and safer. 5 lamps for 3 1/4 hours costs 6d. {Five saver lights in the year 2002 would cost only twice the amount amount despite inflation of other goods at nearly 1000%.}

Other visits were detailed and printed. It was noted that coal in Chester was half the price. £15,000 to £20,000 would be needed for installation.

<u>Watch Committee 7th January 1892</u>

A sum not exceeding £20,000 is to be spent on installation.

<u>Watch Committee 17th February 1892</u>

The council are receiving letters from Electrical Engineers. Three are to be contacted to ask them how they would proceed, what experience they have and what their terms are.

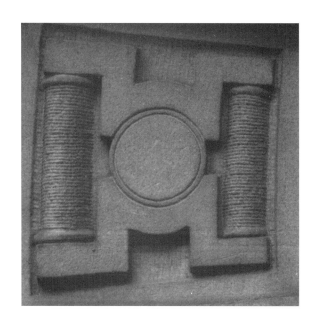

Transformer
Image from the front of the former
Electric Showroom in Foregate Street.

Poles apart

Dr Hopkinson be requested to prepare and submit a report as to the best system to be adopted and site to be selected.

Watch Committee 27th May 1892

Several sites were suggested including Hop Pole Paddock and Dee Mills.

Special meeting of the Watch Committee 7th June 1892

Dr Hopkinson`s report was read.
He considers two types of current and different sites. He recommends the 'excellent' position of Hop Pole Paddock while noting that there may be opposition from the Cathedral authorities. He rules out the Old Workhouse, Sewage Works, and the Tower Field {Water Tower Gardens} as being too far from the city. Sandy Lane and Saltney were not even visited. He suggests a cost for the works of £16,224. {Strangely low considering costs in Brighton £42,000 and West Brompton £70,000 and a yearly bill of £1196-10-0.}

Watch Committee 30th June 1892

C P Goode of Hammond & Co writes
"Dear Sir,
I note your Corporation have consulted with Dr Hopkinson.
Possibly you are aware that he is a low tension man and connected with the three wire system as to which he holds several patents. It is only natural then that he should recommend his own system."

He goes on to say why low tension is not suitable for the city and offers his own company for tenders and continues:
"Personally, I should be extremely sorry to see Low Tension brought to Chester as I feel convinced that the Corporation would find themselves in the same position as Brighton now is, viz: that of being always called upon to provide further capital.
Believe me
Yours very truly
C P Goode"

Hopkinson immediately responded saying that he was not a *"low tension man"* and had sold his patent.

Mr Goode attended the meeting as did Mr Moore of Parsons & Co. Both are asked to tender for works.

Watch Committee 30th June 1892

Hammond & Co, Parsons & Co and various others are asked for quotes.

Watch Committee 14th August 1892

John Rowarth of Brush & Co attended the meeting. They had built stations at Worcester, Huddersfield, Canterbury, Dover and Hastings. Low Tension had failed at Bournemouth. His company supplied lighting at 4 1/2 miles distance and were successful. His attention was drawn to the previous decision to allow tender.

Watch Committee 26th September

Tenders received were adjusted for comparison.
A motion to get Dr Hopkinson to examine the tenders was thrown out. A motion to request Mr W H Preece FRS to examine the tenders was a stalemate. A motion to get an engineer to examine the tenders was passed.

Watch Committee 14th December 1892

It was passed that, subject to price, Mr Preece be instructed to examine tenders.

Watch Committee 11th July 1893

Mr Preece's letters are read. He writes to ask for the tenders to examine but complains of being *"put in opposition to"* Dr Hopkinson and doubts whether they will have any difference of opinion. Moreover *"Hopkinson is the best man in Europe"* and *"a great personal friend"*.

Preece's report
1. He understands that they already have a report by Dr Hopkinson which he has not seen but makes his independently.
2. A list of Electric Works.
3. *"Nothing can prevent Electric Light being the light of the future. It is clean, comfortable, pure and healthy. It does not vitiate the air we breathe. Its effect on the health of large staff in offices so lighted is most marked."*
4. Cost: London supplies electricity at the same rate as gas.
5. The Corporation should be the proprietor.
6. The position of the station should determine the system not vice-versa.
7. High Pressure has to be maintained for 24 hours, low pressure can use batteries.
8. The Market site is too small; the Wharf is not solid; the Hop Pole Paddock is suitable but *"Owing, however to its proximity to your beautiful Cathedral, it would, to my mind, be a pity to place an Electric Light Station there..."*.
9. To supply a full load of 100 kilowatts {10 houses use this nowadays} would cost £13,000 for buildings and plant.
10. Annual costs would be £2,500 equal to revenue.
11. Public Lighting would be an advantage to all classes and would not be to the detriment of poorer members of the

community.

12."*I strongly urge the Committee to look the matter boldly in the face. Electric Lighting is no longer experimental. The prophecies as to its expenses, its dangers, its uncertainties have vanished. It is the light of the future. It will be cheaper than gas, and it will be wanted all over the Borough. The Provisional Order impresses on the Corporation serious responsibilities. Six ratepayers, if they are prepared to guarantee a certain amount can requisition for the light. Hence it is essential to contemplate the spreading of the mains everywhere. The Committee should take a broad view of the question and grapple boldly with it. An expenditure of £15,000 will be ample to commence with, but the buildings and equipment should be so designed as to be elastic and capable of expansion with the growth of the business, a growth which I believe will be more rapid than the most sanguine anticipations of the warmest supporters of the movement.*"

At the same meeting Dr J Hopkinson was appointed Chief Engineer.

Quarterly meeting of the City of Chester 11th October 1893

Letters were read as follows:

Hear electrics go to Hop Pole Paddock hope the walls and cathedral may be spared great degradation that would result
Westminster

Dear Mr Mayor, The Chapter met yesterday to consider the proposal to put Electric Light works on the Hop Pole Paddock, as it manifestly affects the Cathedral as well as the City Walls. I write to request, in the Name of the Chapter, that they would receive a Deputation from the Chapter that they

might present a Memorial on the subject to yourself
and the Corporation. I understand that the Council
meet at 2.30pm tomorrow, and as I am obliged to go
to London I should esteem it a personal favour if you
could receive the Deputation as soon after 2.30 as is
convenient,
Believe me
Yours very faithfully
John L Darby

The Right Worshipful
The Mayor of Chester

*The Very Reverend The Dean, The Venerable Archdeacon
Barber and the Reverend Canon Fielden, attended as a
deputation. The Dean explained that the Venerable Archdeacon
Gore was not able to be present, and read and addressed the
Council upon a Memorial which was as follows:*

The Right Worshipful the Mayor and the Town Council
of the City of Chester
The Dean and the Chapter of Chester Cathedral, having
observed in the Report on Electric Lighting in Chester
that the Hop Pole Paddock is under consideration as a
possible site for the necessary Works, beg leave
respectfully to represent to the Mayor and the Town
Council, that in their judgement it would be a grievous
eyesore and a permanent injury to the City itself if that
site is so used. There can be little doubt that it would be a
constant and serious interference with Divine Service,
and might preclude the possibility of holding the
Triennial Musical Festival, while both the Services in the
Cathedral and the Festival have proved of widespread
interest.
Architecturally the Works would seriously affect the

23

Cathedral which is now such an attractive feature of the City. It may be remembered that the Chapter and the Public have expended no less a sum than £120,000 on the Building and Precincts to make them worthy of their high purpose rendering them as one of the principle adornments of the Ancient City.

The Chapter note that Mr Preece on page 8 of his Report deprecates the site being used because of the proximity to the Cathedral.

The Chapter always have been desirous of the Hop Pole Paddock kept as open space for the benefit of the City at large And they are quite willing to approach the Ecclesiastical Commissioners in order to see whether some substantial step can be taken to place the Paddock in trust for the enjoyment of the Citizens

Signed on behalf of the Chapter capitularly assembled on the 9th day of October 1893

John L Darby D D Dean

The Mayor assured the deputation that the Memorial should receive the careful consideration of the Council.

At the same meeting,
Upon the proceedings of the Watch Committee
It was moved by Mr Alderman W Johnson and seconded by Mr I I Cunnah
That the Hop Pole Paddock be the site for the proposed Electric Light Generating Station
Mr B C Roberts moved and Mr Alderman R Frost seconded an amendment
That the further consideration of the subject be deferred until after the 9th November next.
The amendment being put to the Meeting was lost
The original motion was then put to the Meeting and carried.
{So much for the council's consideration of the Dean.}

<u>At a Quarterly meeting of the Council, 9th November 1893 the Electric Lighting Committee was formed</u>

<u>Electric Lighting Committee 11th December 1893</u>

Sub-Committee to inspect the Liverpool Works next Monday {and do some Christmas shopping at the same time, no doubt}.

<u>ELC 3rd January 1894</u>
The Dean will not remove his objections. After discussion it was concluded that the Council, having settled on the site, it was not for them to deal with suggestions for keeping open space.{Sounds familiar!}

Reports were given on visits to Bradford, Leeds, Preston, Blackpool, Huddersfield, Manchester and Liverpool. Bradford capital was over £50,000.
Mr Hammond at Leeds repeated unhesitatingly his firm conviction that the High Pressure System is the preferable one and named the cost of the Copper Mains as the chief difference financially between the rival systems and that the Low Pressure 3 wire system is commercial only when supplying Current under 1/2 mile distance. He is of the impression that when Incandescent lamps are further improved, more light will be obtained at a cheaper price and *"Gas will be entirely abolished as an Illuminant at some future date".*
Mr Mountain at Leeds would not think of introducing Low Pressure if Suburbs are to be lighted. Preece's estimate is considered too low. Demand for lighting is increasing daily. However, there is still a wide diversity of opinion and dissension over systems and even the mechanical appliances to carry a system out, even though some have been used for years. {Similar confusion arose with computers in the 1980s.}

An interview with Dr Hopkinson (later published by the council) discusses whether there is room for baths and an Electric Station on the paddock, what the best system is, and the cost.

Generator field coil
Image from the front of the former
Electric Showroom in Foregate Street.

Low Tension
INTERVIEW WITH DR. HOPKINSON

By MR. W.H.CHURTON: Q. - Do you consider if we have Baths, as well as Electric light Installation in the Hop-pole Paddock, having regard to the present requirements, and the possibilities for the future, there is sufficient accommodation for both?

A. - There is no doubt about it.

Q. - Supposing we want a second Swimming Bath, have we land enough for that purpose?

A. - I should not like to take less space for Electric Lighting than shown on the Plan - three Engines of 100H.-P. shown on Plan, and room for six more.

(The City Surveyor explained that the Plan showed two Swimming Baths.)

After examination of the Plans -

I have no hesitation in saying that the Hop-pole Paddock is large enough for Electric Light and Baths, even with an additional Swimming Bath.

Q. - Are you of the opinion that any injury is likely to arise to the City Walls, the Cathedral, or any of the adjoining buildings through vibration?

A. - I believe there will be no risk. I don't think anyone could tell from the vibration whether the machinery is running or not, even with a full load on; it all depends on putting in a proper foundation. I have experienced vibration in Vienna, Paddington, and at gatti's, and other places sometimes 100 yards from the station.

DR HOPKINSON explained he had had large professional experience in litigation on the subject of vibration.

By MR. BIRD: Q. - What amount of land do you take up that is not covered by buildings for wires?

A. - we should take the wires in through here (indicating on the Plan); we might also take others through the Walls.

27

By MR. W. H. CHURTON: Q. - We are met by the Cathedral authorities with many objections. One goes to noise; will there be much noise?

A. - We can reduce the noise to a small matter; indeed, it can be easily removed.

Q. - You tell us as our Engineer that there will be no noise that anyone can complain about?

A. - We can avoid it.

Q. - Does it occur to you that the Engines are placed in the best position to avoid objection on the score of noise?

A. - If thought preferable we could move the Engine-house nearer the playground.

By the TOWN CLERK: Q. - In speaking of noise do you include throbbing or droning?

A. - Yes; vibation coming through soil; noise coming through air.

By Mr. CHURTON: Q. - Is it desirable from any point of view that Baths and Electric Lighting Station should be together; and if so, what would be the advantage?

A. - I take it the Baths would require hot water, and this could be provided economically by means of the Electric Lighting Station. It amounts to this, you can get your hot water at very small cost indeed.

Q. - Do you know any other places where they are combined?

A. - No; but other combinations I have met with have been very successful.

Q. - As to economy by combining staff?

A. - Not much in this; you might get a little; the principle benefit would be in providing hot water.

Q. - Could the works be so devised that the chimney could be placed behind high buildings?

A. - There would be no difficulty in doing so by means of a flue.

Q. - As to smoke?

A. - With a Mechanical Stoker and careful attention there

need be no cause for complaint.

Q. - Do you suggest we should adopt the Three-wire System?

A. - Yes.

Q. - To supply the compulsory area in the first instance?

A. - Yes.

Q. - What distance will the three-wire System serve?

A. - Three-quarters of a mile, without any aid.

Q. - Supposing we had to supply the Suburbs of the City, what would you propose?

A. - If the distance were considerable, say a mile and a half, I should put down a Battery in the neighbourhood, and supply that slowly, and so make up by time for the small amount. The time required in labour attending to the Batteries would be small, equal to about half-time of one man. A battery means an Accumulator, which may be placed in a cellar or small chamber; it does not require any machinery.

Q. Would you advise high pressure for that distance?

A. - Certainly not...

By MR HUKE: Q. - If the site were at Sealand would the Low-pressure be best?

A. - I should like to consider the question further before giving an opinion. I should consider the question de novo. I have understood there is not room enough at the Sewage Works for Electric Lighting Station.

The CITY SURVEYOR: That is so unless additional land be bought...

.

By MR W. C. DEELEY: Q. - Supposing the station were on the land lately purchased at Sealand, and we wished to supply the suburbs to the extent of one-and-a-half mile, would you recommend the High-pressure system, and can you give us any idea of the extra cost?

A. - Using High-pressure with alternating current, with three shifts, the main point would be that you would have to work day and night.

Q. - The Three-wire System being patented, has the patent long to run?

A. - It expires July, 1896.

Q. - What Royalty would be payable?

A. - It would be trifling seeing how short a time it will have to run; certainly under £100.

By the TOWN CLERK: If Willans' Engines are used would they take less space than others?

A. - Yes.

Q. - Do you prefer Willans' or Horizontal Engines?

A. - I have no strong opinion; success can be assured with either, and the difference of cost would be small. It is largely a question of convenience.

SURVEYOR: Does DR. HOPKINSON know any reason why MR. PREECE should have reported, in writing, that the Three-wire system will not supply more than half-a-mile distant?

A. - With Low-pressure and Battery you can easily light at a distance of 1 1/2 miles.

ELC 22nd January 1894

Block Plans put forward by the City Surveyor.

Quarterly meeting of the Council 14th February 1894

The minutes of the last meeting having been read, Mr Alderman H T Brown called into question the correctness of the Minute of Resolution passed on the subject of the Memorial of the Dean and Chapter in reference to the Hop Pole Paddock, and after a long discussion put a motion to eliminate the words "The memorial having been further considered". The motion was lost.

A letter was read as follows, viz:
St Werburgh Chambers
Chester 14th February, 1894

Dear Sir,

The Dean and Chapter beg leave to acknowledge the receipt of your letter with respect to the recommendation of the Watch Committee in re Hop Pole Paddock.

They trust that if the Town Council for any reason do not follow that recommendation the offer of the chapter to apply for the sanction of the Ecclesiastical Commissioners to acquire the Paddock as an open space and otherwise to improve the Kaleyard approach will not be overlooked as the Dean and Chapter are ready to make such application when it is open to them to do so.

Yours faithfully
Charles Coppack
Chapter Clerk

The letter was referred to the Improvement Committee.

ELC 16th March 1894

A strongly worded letter from the Dean & Chapter offering to give £1000 to purchase the paddock as open space is read. The Committee resolved that the paddock was still the best site.

Monthly meeting of the Council 11th April 1894

The minutes of the Improvement Committee were read and the correspondence with Mr C Coppack, Chapter Clerk, read and a long discussion ensued when it was moved
That the offer of the Dean and Chapter of £1,000 for the

purchase of the Hop Pole Paddock, subject to the following conditions, viz:
(1) That it never be built upon, and be for ever kept open.
(2) that the Chapter relinquish the Corporation a strip of land 12 feet wide at the back of Frodsham Street if and whenever the corporation require it for the purpose of widening that Street be accepted.
...rescinding the Resolution of the Council of 11th October 1893. The subject was deferred until the next meeting.

Oil-cooled transformer
Image from the front of the former
Electric Showroom in Foregate Street.

High Tension
ELC 22nd May 1894

Mr Roberts had visited Oxford Electric Station and urged the Committee to inspect this high tension generating station.

ELC 7th June 1894

The Visit to Oxford had shown a High Tension system supplying a continuous current equivalent to alternating current. Mr Parker would tender for Chester. The Town Clerk to send a copy of the report to Dr Hopkinson and ask him to reconsider opinions on cost etc.

ELC 18th June 1894

Dr Hopkinson's revised costs read. Resolved that the Oxford system be adopted.

ELC 22nd June 1894

Other sites discussed including the Old County Gaol {where the Queen's School is now}.

ELC 7th September 1894

The Town Clerk reported that it had been intimated to him that the property owners on the South side of Eastgate Street and the East side of Bridge Street are preparing for an installation on their own account being tired of waiting for the Council and in the belief that the Council are not in earnest and that it is useless looking to the Corporation to provide an Installation within any reasonable date.

A letter is read complaining about the length of time Electric Lighting provision is taking. Jos Beckett from a firm in Eastgate

Row complains that, *'The gas is very injurious to fine fabrics + colours, besides being often of poor quality..."*
"It is evident," he states, *"that there is no real wish or purpose to give the City this modern necessity."*

ELC 13th September 1894

Resolved to recommend the Water Tower Gardens as the site. {The swimming baths were later built opposite Grosvenor Park.}

Special Meeting of the Council 19th September 1894

The minutes of the Electric Lighting Committee of the 7th and 13th February having been read as also a letter as follows viz:

From the Church of Jesus Christ assembling in Queen Street Congregational Chapel, Chester, in meeting assembled, to the Mayor and Corporation.

Gentlemen,
Having heard through the Town Clerk that a proposal is before you to acquire land adjoining our property for the purposes of Electric Lighting Station and Public Baths and inviting an expression of our views, we hereby respectfully urge you not to proceed with the proposal.
Without entering at length into reasons for this attitude we realise that on all hands such buildings would be very prejudicial to us as a religious community, detrimental to our buildings and injurious to the neighbourhood.
We suggest that the erection of such works within a few feet at one point would greatly deteriorate our property, and the motion of engines and machinery, with the escape of steam

make the peaceful conduct of Public Worship impossible.
We also greatly fear that the vibration caused by heavy
machinery in rapid motion the stability and even safety of
our building would be jeopardized and many would be
deterred from joining in our services.

We desire further to say that very recently we have spent
about £900 on the improvement of our buildings, and we
beg that nothing may be done that would be a hindrance to
our work as a Christian congregation seeking the moral
spiritual welfare of the community at large.

We are glad to know that you have other sites under your
consideration and trust that one may be determined upon
which will not be likely to interfere to the disadvantage of
enterprize whose interests are so important as those we are
now trying to serve .

Praying that your deliberation may tend to the material
and moral well-being of our ancient City

Signed on behalf of the Members of the Church

James William Clerk. Minister

Chester September 13th 1894

*It was moved by Mr W C Deeley and seconded by Mr George
Bird*

*That the Water Tower Gardens be the site of the proposed
Electric Light Generating Station, and the Committee be
authorised to proceed to establish the Installation, submitting
Tenders, or terms of any proposed contract to the Council in the
usual way.*

After a failed amendment the motion was carried.

ELC 18th November 1894

Dr Hopkinson be instructed to supply plans and specifications with a view to obtaining tenders. The elevation of the Station prepared by Dr Hopkinson was submitted and the committee instructed to inform Dr Hopkinson that the proposed site in the Water Tower Gardens does not call for any ornamental building.

ELC 25th October 1894

Dr Hopkinson asks for a further £250 to prepare fresh plans. He lists costs for buildings £3,000, boilers £1920, 3 large engines £2,250, 3 large dynamos £2320, substation and engineering expenses.
It is resolved that the distributing system be put in Hamilton Place and £250 further fee agreed. *Dr Hopkinson is agreeable to the City Surveyor [I. Matthews Jones] undertaking the preparation of the plans and superintendence of the buildings and street work, the surveyor taking the commission thereof.*

ELC 27th November 1894

Local Government Board set up Public Inquiry before they sanction a loan of £25,000

Dr Hopkinson writes to say he will not modify his recommendations. Another letter discusses tenders. He recommends Siemens and Co. Thomas Parker's tender is also read and, after a lengthy discussion, Dr Hopkinson is asked to meet the Committee.

Monthly meeting of Council 13th March 1895

Electric Lighting Committee authorised to accept the tenders submitted for engines, boilers and dynamos of £8518. However an amendment was then passed asking for tenders for the complete scheme, including running the Installation for one, two or three years.

Local Government Board asked to sanction a £25,000 loan for the same.

ELC 18th March 1895

A letter from Dr Hopkinson states that the difference of opinion between him and the council is so marked it is inexpedient for his connection with the work to continue. The Town Clerk is instructed to inform Dr Hopkinson that the Committee agree and desire his account at his early convenience.

ELC 26th March 1895

Dr Hopkinson asks for his account to be paid in full and reminds the council his commission could be based on his higher estimates but, if paid promptly, he will accept the lower fee: £652-14-6 not withstanding his legal right to claim for commission on the higher estimates if the account is not settled. Tenders are sent to electrical "expert" Professor Kennedy. General specifications prepared by Consulting Engineer Mr R C Crompton who has now withdrawn from the position so that his firm can tender.

Turbine
Image from the front of the former
Electric Showroom in Foregate Street.

Positive charge

ELC 30th April 1895

Lord Kelvin and Mr Gilbert Kapp to be asked if they will examine tenders and their fee.

ELC 30th April 1895

Lord Kelvin's secretary writes to say that Lord Kelvin will examine the tenders for 100 guineas (£105).

ELC 24th May 1895

Report by Lord Kelvin

1) I have carefully examined and considered the nine answers to your invitation for offers in respect to electric lighting for Chester, which I duly received as advised by your letter of the 30th of April, numbered as follows; 1 and 2, Electric Construction Co Ltd; 3 Thomas Parker Limited; 4 Crompton & Co; 5 Manchester Edison Swan Co Ltd; 6 Siemens Bros & Co; 7 Fowler & Co; 8 Brush Electrical Engineering Co; 9 C A Parsons and Co (letter without offer).
Of these numbers 1,3,4 use continuous current exclusively; numbers 2,5,6,7,8,9 use alternative current, except for street lighting by arc lights, with continuous current derived by transformation from primary alternate current, as proposed in some of the offers.

2)The continuous current has important advantages over the alternate current in respect to simplicity, safety, and use of Storage batteries. On the other hand the high pressure alternate current system has been used in many cases of sparse and straggling distribution of the places to be supplied, and in some cases, as, for instance, the City of London Electric Lighting, in which it has been difficult to find a Site for a generating system, at a small enough distance from the region supplied, to be worked advantageously on the low pressure continuous current system. In the case of Chester we have neither of these reasons for choosing the alternate current system: the most distant part of the district of compulsory supply being only 930 yards from the place chosen for the Generating Station, and the main density of the City lying within a distance of 1,300 yards from that Station. I am therefore of the opinion that the low pressure continuous system should be adopted for Chester, with high pressure only for the street lighting by arc lamps, and for supplying by transformation to low pressure, comparatively small demands for private lighting beyond the present compulsory limits. I find this opinion confirmed by a thorough examination in all details of the eight offers received in answer to your invitation. If superior economy, first cost, and working expenses, all considered, were proved in favour of the alternate current system, it might be right to choose it, notwithstanding the reasons for preferring in other respects the continuous current. But the offers you have received prove, on the contrary, a very decided superiority of economy in the continuous current system for the lighting of Chester.

3) Taking first, prime cost, we find the tenders, exclusive of foundations and buildings as follows: Alternate Current Electric Construction Co, £11,755; Manchester Edison Swan Co, £12,466; Siemens & Co, £14,800; Fowler & Co £14,893; Brush (street lighting not included), £ 8,922; Continuous Current: Electric Construction Co, £18,847;Thomas Parker Limited, £14,200. It is to be noticed that the specifications of capacity of engines and dynamos and quantities etc. of underground conductors, for which the tenders have been given are very different and that when these are considered it may be found that the higher tenders are really for more value supplied. This is certainly the case in respect to the two highest tenders. Without, however, going into this comparison we see from the preceding table that the first cost of the continuous system seems to be greater than that of the alternate current by from £2,000 to

£3,000. But now, turning to the offers for working for one, two, or more years and taking the tenders per Board of Trade unit supplied, for as nearly as may be the case of £200,000 units per annum, we find as follows: Alternate Current: Electric Construction Co, 2.625d; Manchester Edison Swan Co, 5d first year, 4 1/2d second year, 4d third year; Siemens Brothers & Co, 3.15d;Fowler & Co 3.3d; Brush Co, 3d. Continuous Current: Electric Construction Co, 2.625d. Thomas Parker Limited 1.78d. We see that every tender for alternate current, except the Electric Construction Company's exceeds the Electric Construction Company's tender for continuous current...and although the Electric Construction Company's tenders for alternate and continuous current are the same, that of Thomas Parker is less than theirs by .84d. There can be no doubt from these figures and particularly from the tender of the Brush Company, who have the greatest experience of all in alternate current lighting, that it is decidedly more costly to annual working expenses than the continuous current. Their estimate exceeds Thomas Parker's by 1.22d per unit.

4) The difference of 1d a unit amounts to £832 per annum on an output of 200,000 units, and as no doubt the Chester Corporation can borrow at 3% the annual interest on £4,000 first cost would only be £120. Thus we see that barely more than 1.7d per unit on the expense of production would compensate to the Corporation an expenditure of £4,000 on the first cost. Considering this, and all the circumstances with reference to upkeep of dynamos, engines, boilers, and storage batteries, I am of the opinion that the direct current will be decidedly more economical for the electric lighting of Chester than any system of alternate current could be. Of the three offers for lighting by continuous current the system proposed by Crompton and by Thomas Parker is to light the central portions of the city on the three wire plan, and the outer portion and suburbs by high pressure continuous current transformed to low pressure continuous current. In the system proposed by the Electric

Construction Company the whole lighting is done by transformation from high pressure to low pressure. In each of the three systems the transforming from continuous high pressure to continuous low pressure is by a method which has been successfully worked in the Chelsea supply, and in the electric lighting of Oxford and Wolverhampton.

5. Considering the circumstances of Chester as described in 2 above, I am of the opinion that the simple three-wire system without transformation from high to low pressure is decidedly the most suitable for the lighting of all the dense parts of the city, and I approve of all the proposals of Crompton & Co and Thomas Parker in respect to the lighting of outlying parts by the high pressure continuous system. I therefore am of opinion that your choice should lie between that of Crompton & Co and Thomas Parker.

6. In respect to Crompton and Company's proposals and the syndicate nearly ready to commence electric lighting referred to in it, I do not know the circumstances sufficiently to allow me to give you any decided opinion. I suppose the syndicate already has a Provisional Order and that the proposal is virtually to take it up from them. If the Corporation is disposed to entertain this proposal it would I think be necessary that they have more information as suggested in the last sentence of Crompton and Company's letter. It seems satisfactory for the Corporation to go on for two or three years accepting light from the syndicate with the prospect at the end of the time of having to arrange for the purchase of the property. It seems to me that it would be better to have the whole system from the beginning in the hands of the corporation, and with the buildings, engines, dynamos and underground conductors provided to their satisfaction and only to arrange for the supply for one two or more years according to the invitation sent by the Corporation for tenders. I therefore do not think it probable that it would be advantageous for the Corporation to adopt such a proposal as that of Crompton & Co but as I have said I do not know the circumstances sufficiently to be able to give a decided opinion.

7. Should the Corporation not decide to adopt Crompton and Company's proposal, the tender of Thomas Parker ought certainly, in my opinion, to be accepted. I have carefully examined his Specification and it seems to me very satisfactory and judicious in all respects. There are some peculiarities in respect to his form of dynamo, and of balancing transformer, which I believe will be found to have some very important practical advantages. The fact that he can undertake the running of the Station for a period of one, two or three years, on the terms stated in full on the   second leaf of his specification, gives me great confidence in recommending that his tender should be accepted.
Kelvin   London   May 11, 1895

It was resolved to recommend the acceptance of Thomas Parker's tender to full council.

Monthly meeting of Council 12th June 1895

Lord Kelvin's report was read. Needless to say, the councillors decided to avoid the pitfalls suggested by Lord Kelvin and took the tender from Thomas Parker & Co. at a total cost of £17,200, exclusive of buildings.

ELC 26th June 1895

The Town Clerk to write to Lord Kelvin and enquire as to who is the best Electrical Engineer to employ. Insurance, inspection and testing for the engines to be taken with the Manchester Steam Users Association.

ELC 12th July 1895

Kelvin writes to suggest: *"Prof. Kennedy, if he can undertake it, would be the best...if Prof Kennedy cannot...Mr Shoolbred, were it not that he is somewhat apt to be unnecessarily troublesome. He would be thoroughly trustworthy and he has large experience... and he has excellent knowledge in respect to Electric Lighting...It would be entirely from his sense of duty to you that he might perhaps unnecessarily make some difficulties with the contractors, but it is a fault on the right side and to be too complaisant(sic), and I think you might yourselves keep the peace satisfactorily..."*

{With a reference like that who needs enemies.}

Alex Kennedy accepts the duties on a 5% commission on the contract. The Committee accept his offer and do not approach Mr Shoolbred. {He is not listed in the British bibliography}. The Board of Trade agree to loan £25,000.

ELC 15th January 1896
Building Plans accepted as long as it is 30 feet from the railway and 10 or 12 feet back from the road.

ELC 20th February 1896
Tenders for building range from £5538 to £7200.

ELC 19th March 1896
The lowest tender is by Thomas Browne. However he wishes to increase his tender by £200 if he is to comply with Messrs Parkers conditions. He first states that Connah's Quay brick would be unobtainable within the four months specified but later says building work can be carried out on overtime rates if the tender is agreed. {He does not say how the brick problem is to be overcome.} His new quote is accepted.

ELC 13th May 1896
Prof Kennedy submits a bill for his first £100

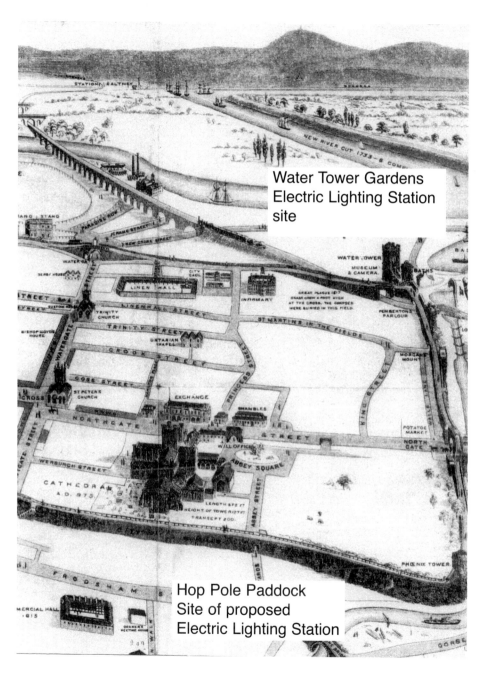

Water Tower Gardens
Electric Lighting Station
site

Hop Pole Paddock
Site of proposed
Electric Lighting Station

The proposed and final sites of the Electric Lighting Station.

Lighting up time

Recollections of Street Lighting in Chester

Mr Samuel Taylor Parry had engineering premises in Princess Street. At the end of the last (19th) century public electricity supply was not available. When Mr B C Roberts (mayor 1895-1896) gave the customary 'At Home' in the Mayor's Parlour in the Town Hall, it was Mr Sam Parry's contribution to light the parlour with electric light, which was something of a novelty. The dynamo was manufactured by Mr Parry in the adjacent workshop across Princess Street and the cables were slung across the street to the Town Hall. Afterwards the dynamo was taken to the museum and in Castle Street was driven by the local steam roller which was parked in Castle Street. It was believed, at the time, that this action was the instigation of the Chester Electricity Department. Later, in the evening a carbon arc-lamp was hung on the flagpole on the Market Square, so Mr Parry could claim to have provided the first electric street lighting [in Chester].

Opposite: Parry's Engineering Works in Princess Street, 1910

Courtesy of Chester History And Heritage Centre. Image Bank Ch0166 (Y1/1/219)

ELC 26th May 1896

After a long letter on lamppost design is read to the committee suggesting looking into taking over the existing gas lamps, setting up a light at each city gate and spacing lights to light Rows from the street, Prof Kennedy is asked to prepare a plan of lighting positions. The charge for units is set at 6d as per Prof Kennedy's letter.

ELC 8th June 1896

Kennedy's positions for arc lamps in Northgate Street, Eastgate Street, Foregate Street and John Street are generally accepted.

ELC 12th June 1896

Prof Kennedy sends wiring rules from Croydon altered to make them suitable for Chester.

ELC 14th July 1896

The Electricity Supply Notice is approved.

A form of agreement and application for electric energy was also approved. Prof Kennedy's plan of lighting sites and the design of a lamppost was also approved.

Lighting Committee 3rd December 1896

The Town Clerk to make plans for the inauguration of the supply on 17th December.

CITY OF CHESTER
ELECTRICITY SUPPLY
FOR LIGHTING, MOTIVE POWER,
COOKING , HEATING, &c.
TO INTENDING CONSUMERS

As the Contractors for the Electric Installation
are now Laying the Supply Maims in the following
Streets, viz.:-
BRIDGE-STREET
GROSVENOR-STREET
PEPPER-STREET
ST. JOHN'S-STREET
EASTGATE-STREET
FOREGATE-STREET
(to opposite St. John's-st)
NORTHGATE-STREET
TOWN HALL-SQUARE
WATERGATE-STREET
AND
NICHOLAS-STREET,
it would be very convenient, and save subsequent
disturbance of the streets, if the occupiers of all
Business Establishments, Banks,Hotels, Offices,
Workshops, &c., also private residents, Clergymen,
Managers and others in charge of Churches,
Chapels, Schools and public or other buildings, in
or near the above mentioned Streets, or the
adjacent Rows, desiring to be supplied, would
forthwith send notification to the Town Hall,
where copies of the necessary wiring rules and
instructions may be obtained (gratis).
The price of supply for lighting will be 6D. PER
BOARD OF TRADE UNIT: special terms for current
required for motive power or other purposes.

The Corporation is prepared to extend the mains
into other streets on receipt of applications for
supply sufficient to warrant the outlay, and invite
applications accordingly.
For forms of application and any further informa-
tion required, apply at the Surveyor's Office, Town
Hall
By Order,
SAML. SMITH, Town Clerk
Chester, July, 1896
Chester, July, 1896

VISIT TO THE ELECTRIC LIGHT WORKS

In the early part of this week, one of our representatives paid a visit to the newly-built electric light station in Crane-street. He was accompanied by Mr John Jones, vice-chairman of the Electric Light Committee, and several other gentlemen and the party were conducted over the works by the resident engineer, Mr Thursfield. The system which has been adopted in Chester, is what is known as a low tension continuous current three-wire system, with a supply pressure of 420 volts, feeding consumers' lamps at a pressure of 210 volts. It is interesting to note that the introduction of the 210 volt lamp is the latest development in electric lighting work. Up until a year ago incandescent lamps were worked at 100 or 110 volts pressure, but on the advent of a reliable 210 volt lamp, several towns changed over from the lower to the higher pressure, and others are now in the process of changing over. On the advice of the Consulting Engineer to the Corporation, Professor Kennedy, Chester has had its electric lighting plant designed and laid down from the start for a 210 supply. The chief advantages of this higher pressure are the large reductions in the cost of the supply mains for a given area, and the much larger area that it is now possible to deal with economically from a low tension station. It will therefore be seen that by coming a little late into the field Chester has reaped all the benefit of the experience in other places, and will boast an installation second to none in the kingdom. The cost at the outset will be sixpence per unit for illuminating power and fourpence for motor power, but it has been decided to allow discount at the rate of £5 per cent. on each quarterly account if paid within 21 days, and a further discount at the end of each year to large consumers according to the following scale:

Units used per Annum	Discount Per Cent
1000 and under 2000	£1
2000 " " 3000	£2
3000 " " 4000	£3
4000 " " 5000	£4
5000 " upwards	£5

The Engine Room

On entering the building the visitor is requested to leave his watch in the office, for the power of electricity in conveying magnetic influence is so great that it will even affect the mechanism of a timepiece in the waistcoat pocket.

The engine room is the one which possesses the greatest

interest to a layman. It is large and well-lighted, but none too commodious for the gathering of to-morrow. Three high-speed engines, two of which are at work, first claim attention. They are of 135 horse-power, each being directly coupled to its dynamo, and being of the double-acting, compound, enclosed type by Messrs. C.E. Bellis, of Birmingham. Each engine, when running at a speed of 350 revolutions per minute, develops 135 I.H.P. with a steam pressure of 150lb per square inch at the engine stop valve. The dynamos have each an output of 104 amperes at 440 volts, or, in other words, each machine is capable of lighting 2,400 eight candle-power lamps.

We have said that only two of the machines are at work, one being kept in reserve in the event of a breakdown, but so great has been the demand for the light that it has been already decided to put down a fourth, and there is room for a fifth, if necessary. In fact the works have been so constructed as to give every facility for extension when required. It is somewhat puzzling to the lay mind to understand the working and province of the little machine which revolves with such rapidity and marvellous smoothness in front of the engines. This is known as the balancing transformer, and consists of two balancing armatures directly connected. It is used to balance the three-wire system, and also to drive the boosters, which are small dynamos on the same shafts as the balancing armatures. The boosters are used to charge the regulating cells of the batteries, and also on occasion, if need be, they can be used to help the batteries to discharge.

From here the current is taken to the switchboard, a wonderful piece of mechanism. The board is studded with a variety of meters, indicators and levers, and standing on the rail gallery in front of it the engineer commands at a glance, and can control, the amount of pressure in all parts of the town.

The Switchboard in the 1940s

The switchboard consists of three enamelled slate slabs carried on an iron frame, and from it the current is carried to the town by means of two main feeders and a third wire feeder which go straight to the Cross.

There the mainfeeders divide, four sub-feeders being run to feeding points in Bridge-street, Watergate-street, Northgate-street, and these feed the distributors to which the consumers' premises are connected. The third wire feeder is at the Cross connected upto the third wire of the distributors. From each of the four feeding points what is called a pilot wire is laid back to the switchboard at the central station, by means of which the engineer in charge can at any time ascertain the pressure of supply at any one of the four points, the pressure at these feeding points being the pressure at which the consumers' lamps are fed.

The mains have been laid by Messr's Callenders Cable and Construction Company, under the superintendence of their resident engineer, Mr. A. Burton. The system is lead sheathed and armoured cables laid direct in the ground. In one corner of the same room is a condenser, to which exhaust steam from the engine is carried. A centrifugal pump, driven by an electric motor, draws the condensing water from the Dee Basin, and returns it again to near the same spot from the condenser discharge tank. The engine can be run either condensing or non-condensing, as the condenser can be shut off and the steam exhausted into the atmosphere.

A travelling crane overhead, capable of lifting an ordinary load of eight tons runs the whole length of the engine-room.

The Boiler House

Passing next into the boiler house, we find three large water tube boilers made by Messrs. Badcock and Wilcox, each capable of evaporating 5,000lb. of water per hour at a steam pressure of 160lb. per square inch. Here, too, there is ample room for extension, space being available for two more boilers. The boilers are fed by two Worthington feed pumps of the horizontal type, each capable of delivering 1,500 gallons of water per hour against the full working pressure of the boilers. The feed-pipe system is in duplicate throughout. The pumps can deliver straight to the boilers, or having pumped the feed water through a Green's economiser, which is placed in the main flue between the chimney stack and the boiler-house. The economiser consists of rows of tubes, and as the water is being pumped through them it is raised in temperature to near the boiling point, as the waste gases from the boilers at a temperature of from 300 to 400 degrees Fah. come in direct contact with these tubes on their way to the chimney. By this means a saving of about ten per cent. in fuel is effected, as, instead of being fed with water at about 60 degrees Fah. the boilers take their feed at a temperature of about 200 degrees Fah.

Finally, in the battery room one finds two sets of E.P.S. accumulators, each consisting of 115 cells, and each battery having a capacity of 300 ampere hours {ten times today's large car batteries} The normal rate of discharge is 60 amperes for five hours, or both batteries together are capable of lighting 800 eight candle power lamps for five hours.

The works also include an engineer's office, test room and general offices. In the preparation of this article, our representative had the courteous assistance of Mr. Clarke, the representative of Professor Kennedy, the consulting engineer of the Corporation.

THE ELECTRIC LIGHT IN CHESTER.
OPENING CEREMONY

The formal opening of the electric light installation took place at the central station in New Crane-street on Thursday afternoon. The company assembled in the engine room, which was not too commodious for the purpose at half-past three. In front of the switch board a dias had been erected, and upon a table in the centre lay the switch-box by means of which the Mayoress was to turn on the light...

LC 23rd November 1897

Professor Kennedy reported that the station was working very satisfactorily and many matters referred to him can safely be left to Mr Thursfield.

LC 4th January 1898

Prof. Kennedy reports that the works, buildings and mains may now be considered as taken over by the Corporation as the contract with Messrs Parker is now complete.

LC 17th January 1898

A reduction in cost will be made to consumers: 5d a unit and 3d a unit for motive power.

LC 28th March 1898

Electrical Power Storage Company contract to maintain Storage Battery is submitted.

LC 27th February 1899

Scheme submitted to supply Chichester Street, Lorne Street, Church St, Garden Lane, Canal St, Walpole St, Bouverie St, Cheyney Lane and Parkgate Road to Cheyney Lane.

LC 28th August 1899

The Assistant Engineer asks for (and is given) a rise in salary to £150 pa stating that: *"I think I am right in saying that there are very few, if any, Electric Lighting Stations in England of the size and importance of Chester, where the Chief Assistant is receiving a salary as small as mine"* and pointing to the large extensions of mains which are still increasing.

LC 15th December 1899

Further engine and dynamo ordered as well as a flywheel to meet the possible requirements for the running of Tram Cars.

LC 5th February 1900

Building and works extension planned at cost of £7,220

LC 1st October 1900

Scheme for lighting Gladstone Avenue, Whipcord Lane, Charlotte Street, Catherine Street and Cambrian View.

LC 7th April 1902
Detailed arrangements for laying supply to power electric tramways. It is also proposed to remove most of the lamps from the route and place the lamps on the top of the trolley line poles. {Chester ran a dozen open-top electric trams on a metre wide tramway with a gradient of less than 1 in 30 from

57

Chester Station to Saltney. They were green and cream with a single light each end. Five new cars were added in 1906. The trams ceased in 1930, to be replaced by buses. The tramway cable brackets can still be seen on the walls of some Eastgate Street buildings. One holds the Grosvenor Hotel sign stable in high winds.}

LC 17th March 1904

Electrical Engineer, Mr Thurston resigns.

LC 31st March 1904

Mr Thurston's solicitors ask for dues to him over several years as Consulting Engineer for works of over £100,000.

City Council 20th April 1904

Lighting Committtee authorised to accept the offer of Messrs Barry Skinner & Co to supply 1000 Porcelain (Conical) Silvered Reflectors, complete with brass springs and washers, &c, for the sum of £42 12s 6d.

Tramways Committee 29th April 1904

DRIVERS AND CONDUCTORS

A Memorial signed by the Drivers and Conductors of the Tramways was read as follows, viz:-

To the Manager   April 27th, 1904
Chester Corporation Tramways

Dear Sir,

We, your humble servants, Drivers and Conductors, of the a
foresaid Tramways Department, do wish to draw your attention to
our grievances, to which we feel sure you will give your best
consideration.

Firstly - That as we have now completed twelve months working of
the electric cars at the exceptionally low wage of 5d. per hour
(Drivers) and 4d. per hour (Conductors), we do now most humbly
ask you if you would influence your Committee to give us a fair
wage of 6 1/2d. per hour for Drivers and 5 1/2d. per hour for
Conductors. Secondly - That we think that we ought to be paid for
10 hours per day on all time bands now in operation, as some
turns only run to 9 1/4 and 9 1/2 hours per day, which takes a
day of 12 1/2 and 13 hours from start to finish.

Thirdly - That we be paid time and a half for Sunday work the
same as all other men are paid.

Fourthly - That the Petition presented 12 months ago will receive
consideration (re one week's holiday with pay).

Trusting that these four items will receive both your and your
Committe's unanimous approval,

We are,

Your obedient Servants

(Here follow 24 signatures)

59

Special Meeting of the Tramway Committee
6th June 1904

RESOLVED - That it be recommended to the Council that the wages of the Motormen be increased from 5d to 51/2d per hour, and the wages of the Conductors be increased from 4d to 41/2d per hour, upon the present system of working, and that this rate be regarded as the maximum rate of pay.

RESOLVED That all the other matters referred to in the above-mentioned Memorial be not entertained.

An electric tram in Eastgate Street
during the early 20th century

60

Britton leads the way

Special Meeting of the Council 26th April 1904

Mr S E Britton is appointed as City Engineer at £300 pa.

LC 25th July 1904

Mr Thursfield settles for £350.

LC 6th March 1911

Plans for use of the Dee Mills for generating electricity by Water Power suggested.

LC 29th May 1911

Dee Mills Power Scheme are given in full with costs, £10,000 with £1,059 yearly operating expenses.

Hydro Electric Generating Station at Dee Mills

The council referred the hydro-electric plans to Electrical Engineer A C Hurtzig who accepted that it was an economic and worthwhile plan. Although a hydro-electric scheme had supplied power to Worcester, Chester had the first hydro-electrical system in Britain dealing with tidal and head waters. Its successful installation influenced the later scheme in York.

Three vertical Gordon Water turbines drove two 225kW Direct Current generators. The surplus night energy was stored in a battery at the Crane Street Works. In 1932 the plant was fitted with a motor convertor for alternating current distribution.

Queen's Ferry Power Station

The station was bought in 1923. Fourteen Lancashire pattern boilers fitted with Bennis Sprinkler Stokers, and Green's Economisers and Superheaters supplied steam at 160 lbs per square inch pressure with a final temperature of 500 degrees F.

This ran three 1500 kW and one 1000kW Turbo Alternators running at 3,000rpm which, in turn, generated alternating current at 440 volts, 50 cycles, 3 phase. Rotary Convertors, and later Mercury Arc Rectifiers, were then installed at New Crane Street to replace the original generating plant.

Excerpts from an article in Chester Courant, June 18th, 1924.

Between 650 and 700 members of the Incorporated Municipal Electrical Association are visiting Chester this week for the 29th annual convention. The president of the Association is Mr S E Britton, Chester's eminent electrical engineer, and the gathering at Chester constitutes a record for the Association... It was expected that Mr Thursfield, formerly Electrical Engineer of Chester, and now with the Leicestershire and Warwickshire Electric Power Co., would attend, but unfortunately he has been prevented at the last moment....

In connection with the convention it is interesting to note that Chester has a unique electrical installation to show to the members. This is the Hydro-Electricity Works, which, as will be recalled, were opened in 1913. These works are an achievement of which Mr Britton and Chester might well be proud, and there is no doubt that the works will be of great interest to the visitors. Chester has now one of the most up to date electric installations in the country. The supply of electrical energy is obtained from the Hydro Works and from the Power Station at Queen's Ferry, the plant in Crane-street not now being used. In fact the plant at Crane-street is being dismantled and broken up. Chester is going ahead and setting an example to other areas in the supply of electric power to the rural districts. In this connection it will be recalled that the supply electricity to Hoole was inaugurated in April 1923; at Blacon, Saughall and Mollington, on Christmas Eve last, and at Upton in March this year....In the course of two years or so the area of Cheshire in the Chester Electricity area will be equipped with electrical energy for all purposes...

Water Power

The president gave some particulars of the Hydro Electric Power Station...the plant had generated 18 million units at a cost of £7446 (.0993d per unit) the interest and sinking fund charges... amounted to £11,026 (.147d per unit)...together .246d per unit. During the same period the generation of the same quantity of electricity by steam cost, for fuel alone, £43,600 (.587d per unit). The water power resources in this country were shamefully neglected.

The Electric Home

The value of electricity in the home is ably demonstrated in the model home at the premises of Messrs Browns & Co, Chester...described by a lady as an improvement on the model home at the Wembley Exhibition.

Sectioned 'Swan' brand electric copper kettle c1921. The first type of kettle to be fitted with a totally immersed heating element thereby doubling the efficiency of electric kettles. Bulpitt & Sons, Birmingham. Prov. pat.33221/21

*The hall, which is brilliantly lighted, contains the slogan,
" A well-lighted hall indicates a warm welcome from within. "
Passing through the hall we came to the dining room, which is
centrally lighted with an up to date installation. The lighting can
be used to light the table only, to light the ceiling only, or to light
the table and the ceiling. In the dining room is an electrical hot
plate, electric fire, electric kettle, electric toaster, and electric
coffee percolator.*

The drawing-room, which is handsomely furnished, proves the value of the use of electricity in the decorative scheme, and shews how, as the slogan has it, "Good lighting helps to furnish the room." The great feature is the number of wall plugs to which lights can be fixed to make reading comfortable in any position. Another feature is the electrically lighted vases. The room also has its electric radiator and hot water jug.

"A well-lighted mirror is my lady's best friend" is the motto in the chief bedroom. In this room, in addition to the central light, the mirror is lighted by three bulbs.

The second room, the maxim for which is "A good light adds to the comfort of visitors." has a similar lighting scheme, and in addition has electric curling irons, electric bed warmer, electric massage set, and electric shaving water heater. The latter is placed in a glass of water, and in three minutes the water is hot enough for shaving.

**Opposite: 'Magnet' electric cooker HO920, 1927
This black cast-iron cooker was manufactured by the General Electric Company of Mexborough between 1925 and 1930. By the end of the 1930s domestic electricity consumers had increased over the decade from one to ten million.**

Features include a double-glazed oven door, enamelled oven lining, three hotplates, thermometer, a two-pin plug and switch for use with auxiliary apparatus eg. an electric kettle or toaster.

The study, too is well lighted, and contains electric cigar and cigarette lighter, while the kitchen, which is recognised as the most important room in the house, will be the envy of housewives. Most kitchens are miserably lighted (sic) but the kitchen in the model home is an exception. Here the lighting is most effective, and is supplied from an enclosed unit. There is also an electric cooker, electric washing machine, which takes all the hard work out of washing day, an electric suction cleaner, and the indispensable electric iron.

Opposite: Wooden domestic washing machine c1920. Electrically driven with a mangle made by Beatty Bros. of Canada. This interesting machine shows how electricity was first used to drive a formerly hand-operated washer. The tub and four-legged dolly are like those of earlier machines. The electric motor is situated in a hazardous position under the tub. Raising the tub lid automatically disconnects the drive to the dolly, the mangle drive is engaged by a handle to the right of the rollers. Sorry, no spin or tumble driers yet.

Alternating Current
In 1930 conversion from direct to alternating current began. A new system of metal filament lights was installed to light the city streets, designed to complement the existing architecture.

Sydney Ernest Britton

Washington Daily News

Friday September 11th, 1936

Even Pigs are Kept Cozy by Electricity Around 'Those Quaint English Farmhouses'

British Delegate Shatters All Illusions about Isle

Sydney Ernest Britton Praises Rural Electrification Here

By MARTHA STRAYER

Come, come, Mr Sydney Ernest Britton, the Republicans won't like you if you cast a British vote for President Roosevelt on account of his rural electrification program.

Britton, a delegate to the Third World Power Conference, is city electrical engineer of Chester, England, on the north boundary line of Wales.

In addition to casting an unrecorded vote for President Roosevelt because he believes in rural electrification, the Chester delegate will destroy your last romantic illusions about quaint British farmhouses with thatched roofs, tallow candles and pigs in dooryards (sic).

LARGEST SCHEME

Why, he says, the farmers around Chester are so advanced that they even heat their pigsties by electricity.

Rural electrification did it, he says. And this is what he has to say about President Roosevelt's rural electrification program:

"Having worked on electrical development for 40 years, it is very satisfactory to me to visit the United States at a time when your President is paying particular attention to rural electrification and has under consideration the largest scheme in the world for

69

public control of rural electrification.

"It seems to me that such a force should be developed by the state for the people, and not by private enterprise."

The British expert yesterday visited the Rural Electrification Administration's model "electric farm" in Virginia.

"I found only three things we don't have on our British electrified farms," he said. "One is the fly electrocutor, another the fence charged with 90 volts of electricity and the third, air conditioning."

He added that electrified farms in Great Britain are so sanitary that they don't have any flies to be electrocuted.

POWER HAIR CUTS

Forty-five per cent of the farms in 144 square miles of territory including Chester are electrified, Britton says.

"We have farms that for six summer months use nothing but electricity," he continues. "They churn, pump, cook, milk by electricity. They even use electric clippers for their cows." {one wonders if this was supposed to say sheep}

Chester furnishes electricity from a publicly owned system to this area, which has a 90,000 population. Farmers pay a fixed minimum rate which within three years repays 60 per cent of the cost of building the power lines.

PAYS FOR SELF

"We find we don't need to go beyond 60 per cent, because the use of electricity always increases the demand and the remainder of the financing takes care of itself over a period of 25 years," he adds.

"British cities may extend power lines to rural communities on authority from the national board of electrical commisioners. They may go into the open market and borrow the money for the financing.

Present rate for such loans is about 3 per cent".

Rural electrification in Great Britain
(Chester & Cheshire Archives CR342/20)

Sydney Britton's paper dealt with the *'development of Rural Electrification in GB, its effect upon the rural community and the benefits to those who make extensive use of electricity'*. He detailed rural electrification in Chester and pointed to the Special Order in 1923 authorising the city to supply 62 square miles followed by another Special Order to supply a further 72 square miles in 1927.

As well as being able to hire electrical appliances, consumers had the option of having complete installations and reliable appa-ratus for a test period of six months, without payment; in Britton's view a prerequisite for developing new uses of electricity in rural areas.

He included agricultural statistics and notes, together with the opinions of 22 Cheshire farmers.

Farmers reported cleaner milk: *"before - with oil lamps - one could not say what the cow was giving and at times the milk must have been unclean"* and *"bacteriologist's reports giving sustained improvements."*

Mr Allwood of Oak Farm, Waverton, 110 acres made a *"Saving in coal £18 per annum due to cooker, radiators and immersion water heater. Milking machine has saved two milkers for 24 weeks at 10s 0d per week and one boy at 8s 0d per week, making a total saving of £52 per annum. Without increasing the number of employees I have been able to add 200 head of poultry, 100 pigs and 10 sows to stock. Everything is done easier and leaves more leisure."*

However, workers were not always laid off. Mr Cornes of Lodge Farm, Crewe-by-Farndon reported that, *"Workers commence at*

6am instead of 5am and finish half an hour earlier" and Mr Eardley of Caldecott Green Farm was happy with the new power because, where *"one man occupied two hours of his time pumping water for the cattle"* this time-consuming job was now done by a motor pump at the touch of a switch, with the result that, *"he does jobs that I used to do, with the result that I have a much more comfortable time..."*

Cable
Image from the front of the former
Electric Showroom in Foregate Street.

Power to the people

In the late 1980s, when development plans were put forward to the residents of the Old Port area of the city, the author asked a council officer, Craig Booton, whether the Electric Light building would be kept and was told that, " some people don't think it is worth saving."

However, Architect Francis Graves, in the Sunday Times of 4th April 1988, described the building as a 'landmark' worthy of incorporating in a city redevelopment.

At the same time, unknown to residents, a competition was being run by the council for a building to replace it. The winning design of three submissions was a '20's style' port building. The developers, F T Patten & Associates, made a planning application to demolish the Electric Lighting Station and replace it with this 'winning design' office block.

Needless to say, once the plans became public there was an outcry. Several Chester residents, including Len Morgan, John Ebo, Jim Mackintosh, Michael Hoddinot and the author each wrote separately to the Department of Media and Culture to have the Electric Lighingt Station listed. However, English Heritage decided that the building was 'not of national importance'. Despite objections by others and a campaign by the Canal Basin Community Forum who raised a petition of 1500 signatures in four days, demolition permission was granted. {Things have not changed, it seems, since the council made a similar careful consideration of the Dean of Chester's appeal not to build next to the Cathedral. See 3rd January 1894.} A Victorian sewer that, by law, could not be built over was given as a major reason for not converting the whole building or using the long facade.

However, at this stage the goverment quango, CEWTEC, that was to have rented the majority of the office block, pulled out and, with the developers now wanting to build houses, the situation could be looked at again.

The Canal Basin Community Forum Action Committee met the developers on site and suggested a solution to the sewer problem, by pointing out that the original Electric Lighting Station consisted of the central five bays with ornamentation, and that the sewer was outside these bays. Chester City Council commissioned a study into whether or not the station could be reasonably incorporated into a housing scheme and this had favourable results. After more lobbying, local councillor, Steve Davies, asked the council to accept Pattens' new application for a housing development including the original Electric Lighting Station and planning permission was granted, albeit with some changes still to be made.

At the request of the CBCF and after the author's research for this book, road names within the new development pay tribute to Chester's electrical engineers, Thurston and Britton.

Generator
Image from the front of the former
Electric Showroom in Foregate Street.

Biographies, and electrical terms

AC or alternating current An electric current that reverses direction with an independent frequency to the circuit. A forward and reverse 'cycle' is a 'period' and the number of periods per second the 'frequency' or periodicity. See CC & DC.

alternator Electrical machine producing an alternating current

ampere or amp The practical and SI unit of current, now the constant current that when maintained in two parallel conductors of infinite length and negligible cross section placed 1 metre apart in a vacuum produces a force of 2 x 10-7 newton per metre between them; formerly a unit of current that when passed through a solution of silver nitrate, deposits silver at the rate of 0.0001118 gram per second.

Ampere, Andre Marie (1775-1836) French physicist.

arc-lamp A light created by the luminous discharge occurring when an electric current flows between two carbon electrodes separated by a small gap. It has a high intrinsic brilliance.

Board of Trade Unit Unit equivalent to one kilowatt hour, or the expenditure of 1,000 watts for one hour.

Britton, Sydney Ernest (1874-1946) Educated at the City of London School, Britton trained with Messrs Crompton & Co in Chelmsford. He was Assistant Engineer at Southampton, Chief Engineer in Barking and Burgh Engineer at Motherwell before his post as City Electrical Engineer in Chester 1904-1946. He planned the construction of the Hydro-electric works at the Old Dee Bridge in 1913. He served on several government boards in World War I and organised the purchase of the Generating Station at Queensferry in 1923 as well as designing a hydro-electric power installation for the North Wales Counties Asylum in Denbigh. He was elected President of the Incorporated Municipal Electrical Association for 1923/4.

A pioneer and enthusiast who believed that electrical power led the way for modern power usage, his rural electrification process involved farmers in finding out their needs. Over 1,000 farms in the area were supplied. He was invited to read a paper on Rural Electrification at the Third World Power Conference in

Washington in 1936. In 1946, still working at the age of seventy years, he died suddenly. S C Harling took over the post.

CC or continuous current A current flowing in one direction, now known as direct current in the UK and US.

Daniell cell A primary accumulator {battery) cell using zinc electrodes in sulphuric acid in a porous pot immersed in a copper pot containing copper sulphate.

dynamo An electromagnetic machine that converts mechanical energy into electrical energy, especially direct current.

electromotive force or EMF The electrical pressure which drives a current through a circuit in opposition to the resistance. The practical unit of EMF is the volt.

Hopkinson, Dr John (1849-1898) Educated in Manchester and Cambridge. He was the manager and engineer in the lighthouse and optical department of Messrs Chance Bros, Birmingham in 1872. By 1878 he was a consulting engineer in London. He patented the three wire system of distribution in 1882 and published, with his brother, a paper on dynamos in 1886. He was a Professor of electrical engineering in King's College, London in 1890: the consulting engineer to the City and South London Railway in 1895. He was killed in an Alpine accident in 1898.

horsepower or HP A unit of power equal to 33,000 foot-pounds per minute, the electrical equivalent being 745.7 watts.

Kennedy, Sir Alexander Blackie William (1847-1898) Educated at Harrow and Oxford. Senior partner in Kennedy and Donkin, civil engineers 1847. Professor of Electrical Engineering at University College, London 1874-89. Consulting Engineer to Westminster, Chester, Edinburgh, Manchester, Calcutta,and Loch Leven. Member of Lord Parker's Committee on Wireless Telegraphy 1913. Explored Petra and was created a Pasha by HM King Hussein 1924.

Kelvin, First Baron of Largs - Sir William Thomson (1824-1907) Scottish physicist attended universities of Glasgow, Oxford and Paris. By the age of 21 he had a dozen papers published. He established the first physics laboratory in Britain, in the firm of Kelvin and White Ltd. Held 56 patents by 1900, six for dynamos and electric lamps. He is noted for his first law of thermodynamics and the Kelvin scale, and pioneered undersea telegraphy.

kilowatt or kW One thousand watts.

kilowatt hour The commercial unit of energy equal to one kilowatt used for one hour.

ohm The practical unit of resistance between two points on a conductor when a constant potential difference of one volt between them produces a current of one ampere.

parallel connection The arrangement of any number of electrical circuits so that the current is divided between them, see series connection.

pressure Electrical pressure is the same as difference of potential or voltage.

rheostat Component where introduced resistance is readily variable.

series connection the arrangement of several circuits so that the current passes through them all in succession.

SI unit abbreviation for Système International, a metric system of standard units.

Thursfield, F City Electrical Engineer 1898-1904

transformer A device used to change the voltage of alternating current without moving parts by the use of coils.

turbine A machine where the kinetic energy of a moving fluid is converted into mechanical energy by rotating a bladed rotor.

V or volt The practical unit of electrical pressure required to drive a current of one ampere through a resistance of one ohm.

Volta, Count Alessandro (1745-1827) Italian physicist who contributed to the theory of current electricity.

watt The practical unit of electrical power, or the rate at which work is done by a current of one ampere at a pressure of one volt.

Watt, James (1736-1819) Scottish engineer and inventor who improved the steam engine.

Daniell cell
Image from the front of the former
Electric Showroom in Foregate Street.

OTHER BOOKS AVAILABLE FROM GORDON EMERY

Cheshire
Curious Chester: Gordon Emery £14.95
The Boom of the Bitterbump: The folk-history of
                 Cheshire's Wildlife Roger Stephens £11.95
Chester Inside Out Gordon Emery £5.95
          (Hardback limited edition £12.95)
The River Gowy, Source to Sea Pat Bradley £7.50
Miller of Dee: The Story of Chester Mills and Millers, their Trades and Wares, the Weir, the Water Engine and the Salmon Roy
                            Wilding £9.99
Poems on Dee Philip Higson £5.00
Hidden Highways of Cheshire:Ten Circular Walks exploring Roman Roads, Salters' Ways, Lost Lanes, Medieval Roads, and a complete Roman Road RJA Dutton £9.99

North Wales

Underground Clwyd Cris Ebbs £9.99
Curious Clwyd Gordon Emery £11.95
Curious Clwyd 2 Gordon Emery £11.95
Hidden Highways of North Wales RJA Dutton £9.99
Guide to the Maelor Way Gordon Emery £7.95
Daywalks, Vale of Llangollen Gordon Emery & John Roberts £4.95
Family Walks in the North Wales Borderlands Gordon Emery £5.95
Family Walks on the North Wales Coast Gordon Emery £5.95
Family Walks in Anglesey Laurence Main £5.95
Family Walks in Snowdonia Laurence Main £5.95
       Please enquire for Family Walks nationwide

Walks in Clwyd: 35 booklets 99p each (send SAE for full list)

Books can be ordered from any bookshop or by post (include £1 p+p) from Gordon Emery, 27 Gladstone Road, Chester CH1 4BZ

Rheostat
Image from the front of the former
Electric Showroom in Foregate Street.